Voyager Passport C™

D1302914

This book belongs to

_____

Photo and Art Credits

Cover: Jeff Hunter/Getty Images

Title Page: Jeff Hunter/Getty Images

Adventure 1: 1, Punchstock

Adventure 2: 29, Dave Nagel/Getty Images; 33, © Fioresco Productions/Corbis, Photodisc, Photodisc Blue/Getty Images, Digital Vision/Getty Images; 34, Victoria Yee, The Image Bank/Getty Images; 35, © Bruce Smith/Corbis; 40, C Squared Studios, Photodisc Green/Getty Images, Ryan McVay, Photodisc Green/Getty Images; 41, Peter Rees, StockFood Creative/Getty Images, Gary Buss, Taxi/Getty Images; 47, Peter Cade, Photodisc Red/Getty Images, Dr Gopal Murti, Visuals Unlimited/Getty Images, Tongro Image Stock/Alamy; 48, Photodisc, Photodisc Green/Getty Images, Hitoshi Nishimura, Taxi Japan/Getty Images, Photodisc Collection, Photodisc Green/Getty Images, Redcovercom, Red Cover/Getty Images, Tim Ridley, Dorling Kindersley/Getty Images; 49, Steve Gorton, Dorling Kindersley/Getty Images, Tim Platt, Iconica/Getty Images, Spike Mafford, Photodisc Green/Getty Images, Douglas Armand, Photographer's Choice RR/Getty Images, Photodisc, Photodisc Blue/Getty Images; 51, Jenny Acheson, Riser/Getty Images, Steve Cole, Photodisc Green/Getty Images, Nicholas Rigg, Photographer's Choice/Getty Images, Philip J Brittan, Photonica/Getty Images

Adventure 3: 59, Ian Mckinnell, Photographer's Choice/Getty Images, Time & Life Pictures/Getty Images; 61, StockTrek, Photodisc Green/Getty Images; 62, Astromujoff, The Image Bank/Getty Images; 63, Space Frontiers/Stringer, Hulton Archive/Getty Images; 65, Justin Sullivan/Getty Image News/Getty Images, AP Images, Tom Schierlitz, The Image Bank/Getty Images; 67, © Ken Redding/Corbis, Ryan/Beyer, Stone Photographer/Getty Images; 68, H Armstrong Roberts, Retrofile/Getty Images, © H. Armstrong Roberts/Corbis; 69, Thomas Northcut, Photodisc Green/Getty Images, © Larry Williams/Corbis, Digital Vision/Getty Images; 73, © Burstein Collection/Corbis, © CORBIS; 75, Harald Sund, Riser/Getty Images, Matthias Breiter, Science Faction/Getty Images; 76, Frans Lemmens, Iconica Photographer/Getty Images; 77, George Lepp, Riser/Getty Images; 79, After Gallo Gallina, The Bridgeman/Art Library/Getty Images, Kevin Summers, Photographer's Choice Photographer/Getty Images; 81, © North Wind Picture Archives/Alamy; 82, MPI/Stringer, Hulton Archive/Getty Images; 83, Ryan/Beyer, Stone/Getty Images

Adventure 4: 85, Joel Simon, Digital Vision/Getty Images; 87, © Debra Behr/Alamy; 89, Stephen Frink, Digital Vision/Getty Images, George Doyle, Stockdisc Classic/Getty Images, © bobo/Almy; 90, Sisse Brimberg, National Geographic/Getty Images; 91, Flip Nicklin, Science Faction Photographer/Getty Images; 95, Eric Meola, Iconica Photographer/Getty Images; 96, Natphotos, Digital Vision/Getty Images, Jim & Jamie Dutcher, National Geographic/Getty Images; 97, Paul Nicklen, National Geographic/Getty Images; 101, Don Farrall, Photographer's Choice RF/Getty Images, George Lepp, Stone/Getty Images; 103, Digital Vision/Getty Images, Livia Corona, Stone/Getty Images; 104, © Clarke Conde/Alamy, Livia Corona, Stone/Getty Images; 105, © Dan Guravich/Corbis; 107, Michael Poliza, Gallo Images/Getty Images

Adventure 5: 113, Hill Street Studios, Blend Images/Getty Images; 121, Howard Grey, Digital Vision/Getty Images, John Walmsley © Education Photos/Alamy; 129, davies & starr, The Image Bank/Getty Images, C Squared Studios, Photodisc Green/Getty Images, Dave Bradley Photography/Getty Images, Nichola Evans, Iconica Photographer/Getty Images, James Woodson, Digital Vision Photographer/Getty Images, Jan Stromme, Photonica/Getty Images, © Juncal/Alamy; 135, Jack Hollingsworth, Photodisc Green/Getty Images, © Brand X Pictures/Alamy, © Tom Payne/Alamy; 137, Dick Luria, Photodisc Green/Getty Images, Don Farrall, Photodisc Green/Getty Images, VisionsofAmerica/Joe Sohm, Photodisc Red/Getty Images; 138, Stewart Cohen, Blend Images/Getty Images, JGI, Blend Images/Getty Images, © Photick - Image and Click/Alamy; 139, John Foxx, Stockbyte Silver/Getty Images, Jenny Acheson, Riser Photographer/Getty Images, Tanya Constantine, Digital Vision/Getty Images

Adventure 6: 141, Gail Shumway/Getty Images; 143, Bob Stefko, Photographer's Choice/Getty Images, Thomas Northcut, Photodisc Red/Getty Images, Roy Toft, National Geographic/Getty Images, Frank Schwere, Photonica/Getty Images; 145, PhotoLink, Photodisc Blue/Getty Images, © BananaStock/Alamy, © Chuck Place/Alamy; 146, Nick White, Digital Vision/Getty Images, © David Tipling/Alamy; 147, Kevin Schafer, Photographer's Choice RF/Getty Images, Flying Colours, Iconica/Getty Images; 149, A Witte/C Mahaney, Stone/Getty Images, Georgette Douwma, Photographer's Choice/Getty Images; Brad Wilson, The Image Bank/Getty Images; 160, Gail Shumway/Getty Images; 161, Veer Christopher Talbot Frank, Photonica/Getty Images; 163, © Ralph A. Clevenger/Corbis

Passport C

Table of Contents

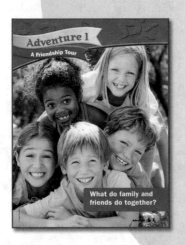

Adventure 1
A Friendship Tour

Adventure 2
Right Choice

Adventure 3
Historical Ride

Adventure 4
Out and About

Adventure 5
Connecting with Kin

Adventure 6
The Big Outdoors

Support Materials

Adventure Map

Adventure 1

A Friendship Tour

What do family and friends do together?

Word Works

Word Reading

A

fan   fat   man   mat

Nan   Nat   ran   sat   tan

Sight Words

B

to   the   on   you   it

Sentence Reading

C

Nat sat <u>on</u> <u>the</u> tan mat.

<u>You</u> ran <u>to</u> <u>it</u>.

<u>The</u> fat ram ran <u>to</u> <u>the</u> man.

Sam and the Family

Sam ran to Nan. Sam ran to Mom. Sam sat on the mat. Sam ran out.

Nat ran to Sam and Dad. "You are it, Sam," said Nat.

Word Works

Letter and Sound Identification

A

d	D	l	g
I	A	a	i

Word Reading

B

dig   mad   fit   and   sad

sat   man   lid   lit

Sight Words

C

for   they   are

to   the   on   you   it

Circus Fun

Dad, Sam, and Gil sat on the bus. They
fit on it.

"Sam, the fat man is sad," said Dad.

They did fit, but it did not have gas!

Word Works

Word Reading

A

beg	met	red	set	hen	fed
hot	sob	not	hog	cot	log

Sight Words

B

said	his	was	as
you	they	for	are	the

Sentence Reading

C

Bob fed <u>his</u> hen.

<u>The</u> hog <u>was</u> not on a log.

<u>They</u> <u>said</u>, "Get in!"

A Card for Bob

Ben had a card for Bob. "It is a party," said Ben.

"It has a cat and a dog!" said Bob. "I can go!"

Word Works

Letter and Sound Identification

A

u   w   p   k   v

U   e   b   P   K

Word Reading

B

mud   cup   bus   plus

slip   grab   step   drop

Sight Words

C

he   that   with

was   as   for   are   said

A Pet Party

Kim let Pug flip on the step. Pug has
a vest.

Ben had to grab his pet. His pet can
skip fast!

The dog can spin on a spot. A pet party
is fun!

Quick Check

Letter and Sound Identification

A

1. w a b	2. t u g	3. k o M
4. i a e	5. S e T	6. h a e
7. o i u	8. a e i	9. i o u

Word Reading

B

1. fin flap flop	2. cup skip cap	3. him hip hop
4. dug dig dog	5. sat sit set	6. drop grip drip
7. cram crib crab	8. spot slip slap	9. pan plan pet

Sight Words

C

_____ the	_____ as	_____ on	_____ was
_____ they	_____ you	_____ with	_____ are
_____ it	_____ to	_____ said	_____ his
_____ for	_____ he	_____ that	

Comprehension Check

Draw lines to match the sentences to the pictures.

A Pet Party

Kim let Pug flip on the step.

Pug has a vest.

Ben had to grab his pet.

His pet can skip fast!

The dog can spin on a spot.

A pet party is fun!

Write another sentence for the story. Draw a picture to go with your sentence.

_____

_____

Word Works

Word Reading

A

pass   yell   zip   stiff

jet   buzz   box   rug

Sight Words

B

we   be   put   do

said   they   or   you   that

Sentence Reading

C

He will <u>put</u> on the cap.

His jet will <u>be</u> red.

"<u>We</u> can help <u>you</u> <u>do</u> a lot," <u>they</u> <u>said</u>.

<u>We</u> can run to the box.

Tad and Gus Help

"We can help Mom. Get the big box of Zap," said Tad.

"Do not put in a lot," said Gus.

"Yes, fill up the cup," said Tad.

They had to fix the problem fast!

Word Works

Letter and Sound Identification

A

st	sl	sk	sp
dr	fr	gr	br

Word Reading

B

best	belt	hunt	band
jump	lift	lost	help

Sight Words

C

have	your	from	or	one
put	do	we	you	his	be

The List

"Time to help a lot. I have a big list,"
said Dad.

"I can trim," said Dad. "Tad can lift. Gus can sort."

"The tan belt and red hat are your gift!"
said Dad.

Word Works

Word Reading

A

melt   skid   draft   sport

blast   flop   stomp

Sight Words

B

this   of   what   were

from   on   or   your   one

Sentence Reading

C

Is <u>this</u> a red sled <u>or</u> a pink <u>one</u>?

The sun will melt <u>what</u> is in the glass.

<u>What</u> is <u>your</u> best sport?

<u>Were</u> you thinking <u>of</u> me?

On Top of a Hill

Meg and I have fun. I stomp and slip.
Meg will tug the sled. This is a big hill.

I start. The sled can go fast. Plop! Meg is
a good pal.

Word Works

Letter and Sound Identification

A

ck	br	fr	r	sk
a	e	i	o	u

Word Reading

B

black   pack   clamp   skip

belt   snack   craft

Sight Words

C

this   of   what   were

one   with   they

Family Day

The Beck family can toss the ball at a park.

The Ross family can make a craft. Jack
will snip and cut one stick.

The Vang family must lift the big pack.
"Will you snack with us?" they ask.

Quick Check

Letter and Sound Identification

1. a e i	2. o e u	3. e i o
4. w y v	5. d g b	6. st sl sm
7. cl cr sl	8. gr gl dr	9. ck cr cl

Word Reading

1. pack pick back	2. stump stamp stomp	3. grill grab grip
4. slick stick sick	5. clam slam cram	6. back bump dump
7. snack sack snap	8. brand bad band	9. lift lit left

Sight Words

_____ the	_____ one	_____ be	_____ are
_____ they	_____ what	_____ from	_____ his
_____ it	_____ you	_____ your	_____ this
_____ for	_____ to	_____ were	_____ or
_____ as	_____ he	_____ said	_____ of
_____ we	_____ on	_____ that	_____ put
_____ have	_____ with	_____ was	_____ do

What choices did you make today?

Word Works

Word Building

A

dog	class	stick	drum	fan
dogs	classes	sticks	drums	fans

Sight Words

B

make   use   out

the   your   to   they   it   with

Sentence Reading

C

<u>The</u> foxes get <u>out</u> of <u>the</u> dens.

We <u>use</u> big sleds <u>to</u> drag <u>the</u> logs.

<u>They</u> <u>make</u> lunches for many classes.

©Voyager Expanded Learning, L.P.

Listen to the Sounds

Rum! Tum! Tum! The kids hit drums. It is a big sound. Your ears can hear it. Fred can strum a song. Fred can make a soft sound. Dogs bark. Bees buzz. Glasses clink.

Stop! Let your ears pick up the sounds.

Word Works

Letter and Sound Identification

A

m	p	r	l
sh	ck	sn	cr

Word Reading

B

shell	clap	dish	snap
mash	trash	fish	shack

Sight Words

C

she   her   their

are   for   this   they   your   was

Use Your Senses

Mel can use her eyes. She can
see pets. She can wish for a fish.

Ben can rub and pet his dog.
This dog is soft.

Tim wants to have a snack. His pet can smell the snack. His pet wants to taste the snack!

Word Works

Word Reading

A   past   pest   slip   slap   stomp   stamp

Sight Words

B   some   into   there

     you   on   that   for   his   of

Sentence Reading

C   We helped him get <u>into</u> the shop.

She wished <u>for</u> <u>some</u> red socks.

Trent fell <u>on</u> <u>that</u> and landed <u>there</u>.

The man filled <u>some</u> <u>of</u> the boxes.

Eat for Energy

Some kids yelled to Fran. "Kick this ball with us!" But Fran just wanted to plop into a big, soft bed.

Fran felt her stomach. Can a snack help?

She picked up a plum. The plum helped! She rushed out and kicked.

Word Works

Letter and Sound Identification

A

th   sh   ck

Word Reading

B

thing	math	cloth
shut	rash	fresh
deck	thick	rock

Sight Words

C

each   many   like

be   he   said   have   or   were

You Can Pick the Best!

Fran is picking. Will she pick fruit and milk? Will she pick chips?

Fran must get energy from food. Fran must use it when she is jumping, kicking, and playing.

Brent is picking food like plums and milk. Brent picks the best.

Quick Check

Letter and Sound Identification

A

1. th	tr	ing	2. sn	sh	th	3. ck	x	g
4. sh	sn	sp	5. st	sl	sk	6. bl	cr	cl
7. dr	br	pr	8. sh	sp	sl	9. cr	gr	gl

Word Reading

B

1. bats	cash	class	2. lash	lock	last	3. rock	block	rob
4. snap	tack	trick	5. slap	ship	drip	6. fish	frill	fresh
7. bath	mats	math	8. thick	grin	thin	9. sting	bring	stump

Sight Words

C

___ make	___ out	___ use
___ she	___ her	___ their
___ some	___ into	___ there
___ each	___ many	___ like

Comprehension Check

Draw a line to match each set of sentences to the correct picture.

Use Your Senses

Mel can use her eyes.
She can see pets.
She can wish for a fish.

Ben can rub and pet his dog.
This dog is soft.

Tim wants to have a snack.
His pet can smell the snack.
His pet wants to taste the snack!

Write another sentence for the story. Draw a picture to go with your sentence.

_____

_____

Word Works

Word Reading

A

patch	fetch	stitch
which	when	whiz
chop	chest	much

Sight Words

B

how　　so　　would

are　　one　　of　　it　　he　　from

Sentence Reading

C

I can toss the hat <u>so</u> <u>he</u> can catch <u>it</u>.

Fred asked, "<u>How</u> can <u>he</u> stitch this cloth?"

When <u>would</u> you like the red chest?

<u>How</u> will you chop the logs?

Surprise Sounds

Mitch had pop with lunch. So, Mitch had to belch a bunch! Mitch held his belches in. When he did, Mitch got the hiccups! How can he get rid of his hiccups?

Chet had a plan. He would scare him. "Boo!" yelled Chet. Mitch jumped. "Watch it!" Mitch said. Mitch got goose bumps! His hiccups stopped. Now Mitch sneezes!

Word Works

Letter and Sound Identification

A

qu	wr	kn	ck
sh	wh	th	ch

Word Reading

B

wren	wreck	wrong	wrath
quill	quiz	quip	quest
knit	knelt	knock	knob

Sight Words

C

way   people   water

from   what   we   there   use

©Voyager Expanded Learning, L.P.

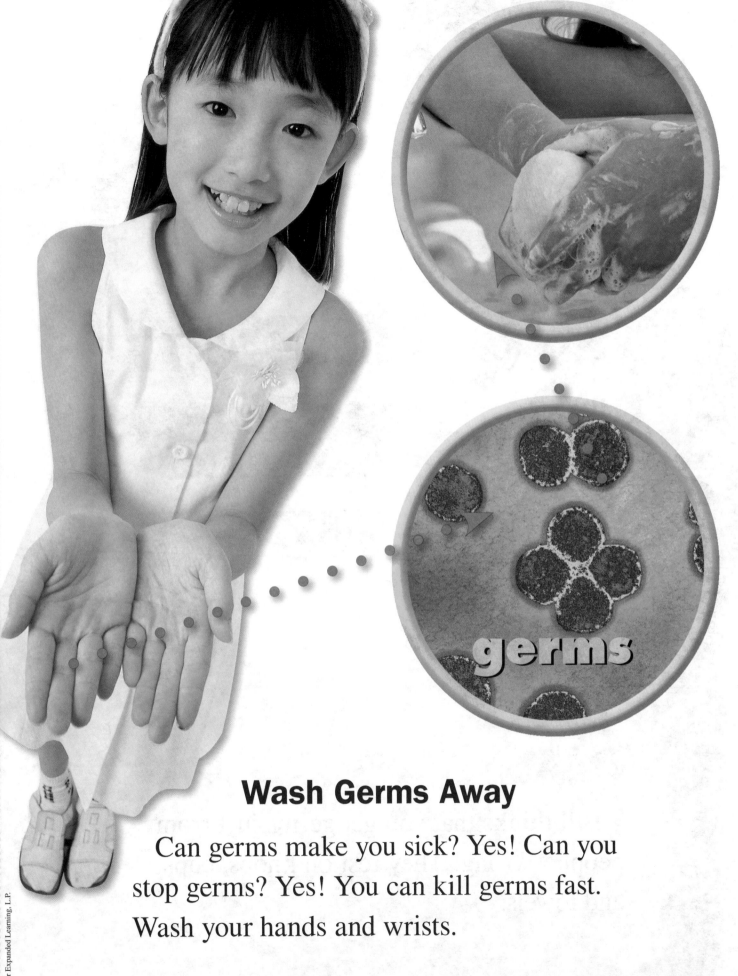

germs

Wash Germs Away

Can germs make you sick? Yes! Can you stop germs? Yes! You can kill germs fast. Wash your hands and wrists.

Bill thinks that you get germs just from people. Wrong! They rest on knobs, cups, and towels.

When should you wash?

When should you wash your hands with hot water? Why do you wash your hands?

Word Works

Word Reading

A

cool	noon	soft	soon
sock	sack	fool	pond

Sight Words

B

first   now   may

each   have   as   there   one   or

Sentence Reading

C The full moon is up <u>there</u>.

I lifted the hot dish <u>first</u>, then I put it in a cool spot.

You can <u>have</u> red boots <u>or</u> tan socks.

<u>Now</u> I must be <u>there</u> by noon.

CAMP IS COOL!

I am back from sports camp! I had to shoot a ball at the hoop. We swam in the pool. We had a race. I ended first. Look at this cool pin that I won!

Camp sports are such fun. Now I want to go back to that camp soon.

Word Works

Letter and Sound Identification

A

ee	a	oo	e	o
th	sh	ch	wh	kn

Word Reading

B

week	keep	sleep	deep	steep
shoot	champ	flash	spool	snoop

Sight Words

C

call   about   part

she   what   was   how   so   we

©Voyager Expanded Learning, L.P.

Lee Goes to Camp

Mom sent Lee to camp. "This is your green camp shirt," said Pam.

What a fun week! Lee sped up steep
rocks. She swam in a deep pool.

"How do you feel about camp?"
asked Mom.

"I met lots of cool kids there,"
said Lee. "But now I need sleep!"

Quick Check

Letter and Sound Identification

1. tch st wr	2. sk ch ck	3. ee es ed
4. qu oo ee	5. sh th wh	6. th tr st
7. wr ink wh	8. tch sh st	9. cr dr qu

Word Reading

1. tree the trick	2. stamp stitch stack	3. wrap whip rap
4. knock knob nick	5. crash fish flash	6. which mash much
7. quill spell spool	8. quilt quest cast	9. catch clap cash

Sight Words

___ there	___ into	___ make	___ her
___ she	___ use	___ now	___ like
___ their	___ way	___ each	___ call
___ out	___ people	___ how	___ water
___ so	___ many	___ about	___ first
___ would	___ some	___ may	___ part

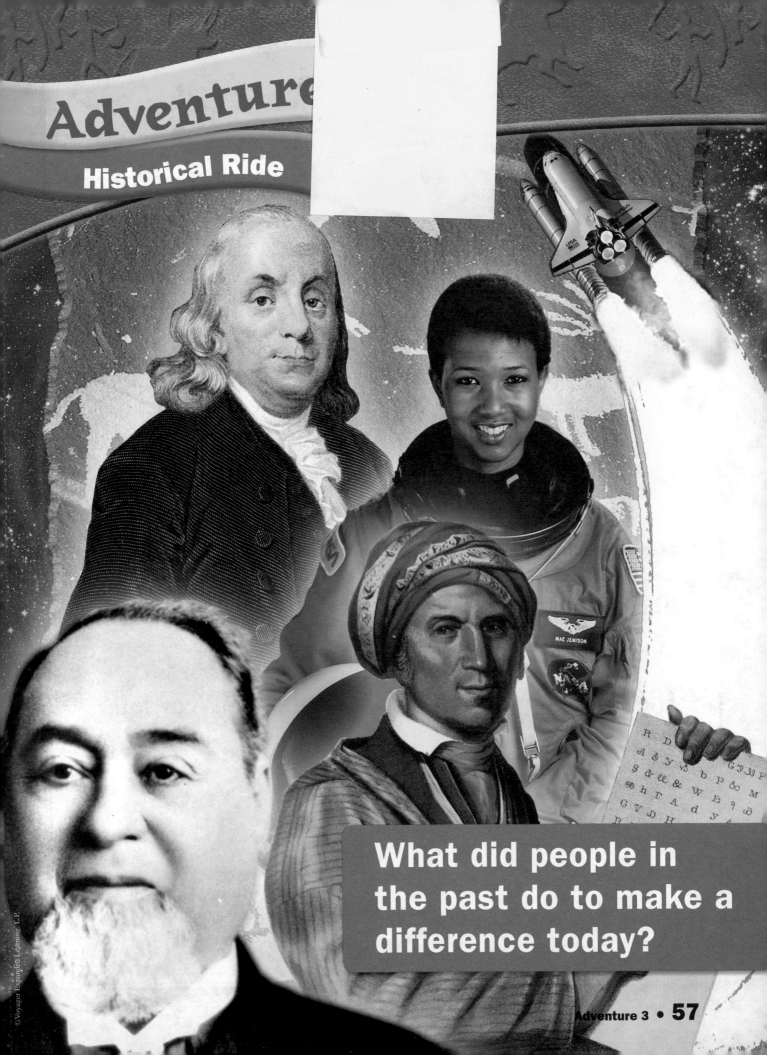

Adventure

Historical Ride

What did people in the past do to make a difference today?

Word Works

Word Reading

A

stay   way   play   sway   say

teeth   ship   plan   champ   swish

Sight Words

B

who   could   words

that   they   how   were   into   was

Sentence Reading

C She <u>could</u> stay and play all day.

<u>Who</u> will play on a stack of hay?

His <u>words</u> <u>were</u>, "Stay off the wall or you may fall."

Mae Jemison, Astronaut

Written by Ava Santos

When Mae was small, she played. "What is in space?" she asked. But men went in space then.

This girl grew up. She liked to think. She had much skill and luck. She could do a lot. People said, "You can zoom to space in a ship. Will you go? Say yes!"

She would go! The ship blasted way up. Then she said, "I did it!"

Word Works

Word Reading

A

neat   spoon   teal   gray   heap

wheat   green   reach   ray   reap

Rule-Based Words

B

ride   wade   brave   shade   home

Sight Words

C

by   than   come

with   he   this   out   her   would

A Brave Space Team

An odd shape is up in space. This odd shape is the space station.

A brave team will ride on a shuttle to a home in space.

The team will eat and rest. The team will run each test and fix many problems. Do you want to take a spot in space?

Word Works

A

cook   shook   tick   nook   trip

skunk   brook   speak   hood   steep

Sight Words

B

want   little   know

were   said   use   she   out

Sentence Reading

C She said, "Look out! It is a little skunk!"

The sheep were climbing on rocks and steep hills.

We were going to shop, but we had to stay home.

People want to know the cook.

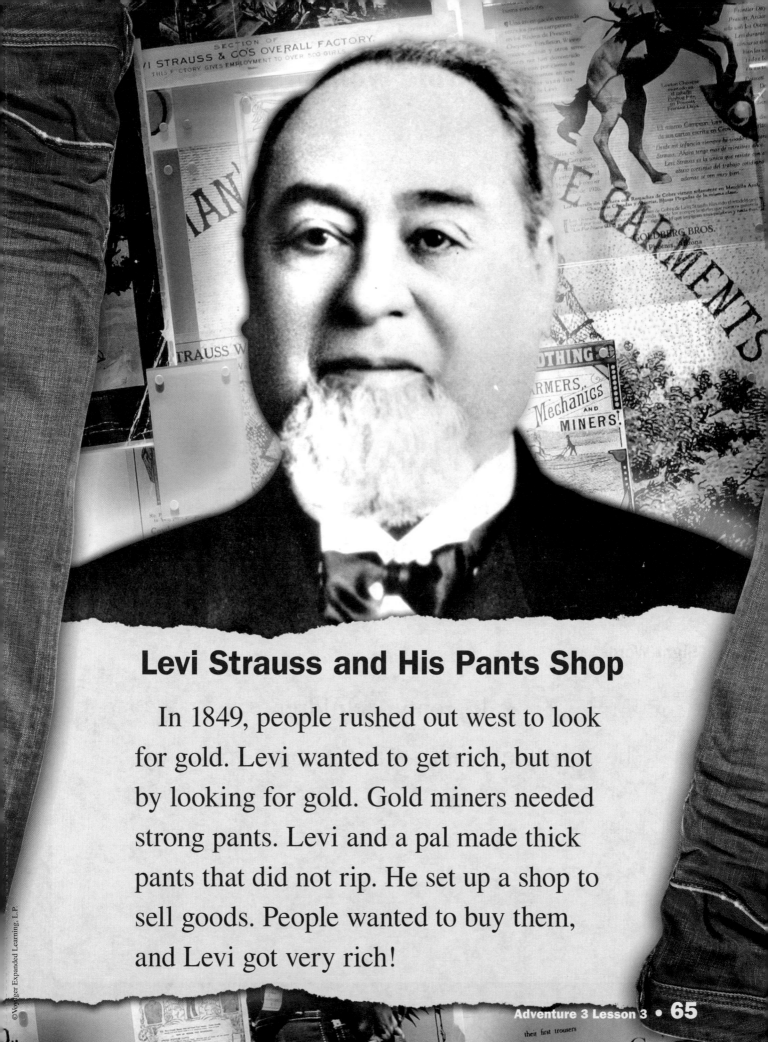

Levi Strauss and His Pants Shop

In 1849, people rushed out west to look
for gold. Levi wanted to get rich, but not
by looking for gold. Gold miners needed
strong pants. Levi and a pal made thick
pants that did not rip. He set up a shop to
sell goods. People wanted to buy them,
and Levi got very rich!

Word Works

Word Reading

A

speech   scoop   streak   stray

root   clear   wheel   good

Word Building

B

save   saving   saved

bake   baking   baked

mine   mining   mined

pile   piling   piled

Sight Words

C

all   only   children

be   people   one   was   what   your   by

Jeans for All Times

Written by Eddie Lee

Do your classmates like jeans? In the past, only men would wear jeans. Workers on ranches liked jeans. The pants lasted a long time.

Then moms and dads let children play in jeans. But they did not think that jeans were good for school.

Now people think jeans are good for play, work, and school.

Quick Check

Letter and Sound Identification

A

1. oo ee o	2. ea ay oo	3. wh wr m
4. th tr wh	5. br wh wr	6. a ea ck
7. ing ck g	8. qu oo ck	9. ea ay a

Word Reading

B

1. cook rock wreck	2. late trick tray	3. bump bug band
4. stay slept stale	5. creak clock crook	6. rate read red
7. lake look lock	8. sick slit sink	9. hang hand hack

Sight Words

C

___ by	___ children	___ come
___ words	___ could	___ only
___ all	___ than	___ little
___ want	___ who	___ know

Comprehension Check

Draw a line to match each set of sentences to the correct picture.

Jeans for All Times

Do your classmates like jeans? In the past, only men would wear jeans. Workers on ranches liked jeans. The pants lasted a long time.

Then moms and dads let children play in jeans. But they did not think that jeans were good for school.

Now people think jeans are good for play, work, and school.

Write another sentence for the story. Draw a picture to go with your sentence.

_____

_____

Word Works

Word Reading

A

race   cell   cent   ice

gem   gel   page   huge

Sight Words

B

other   number   write

you   have   words   about   some   could

Sentence Reading

C

Gene and the <u>other</u> man will race home.

We <u>have</u> a huge <u>number</u> of gems.

<u>You</u> must each <u>write</u> <u>about</u> six <u>words</u> on the page.

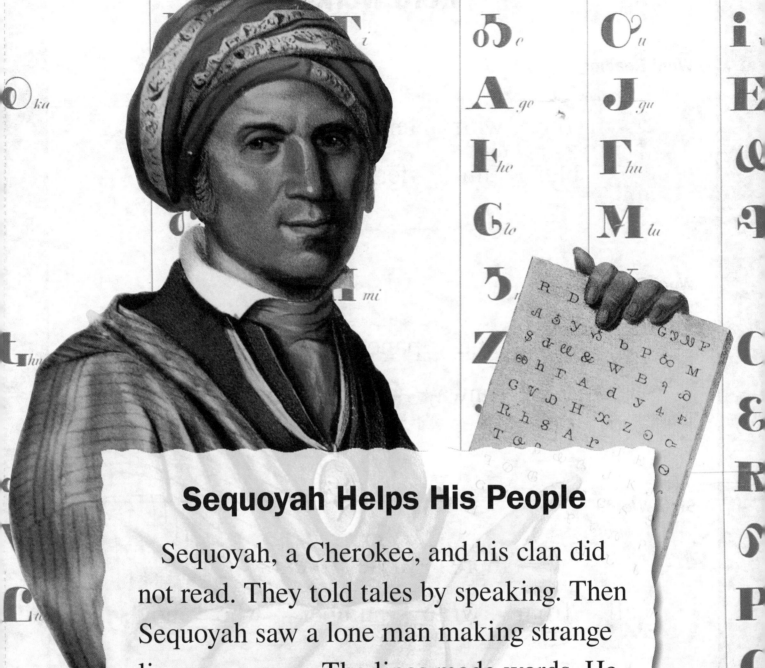

Sequoyah Helps His People

Sequoyah, a Cherokee, and his clan did not read. They told tales by speaking. Then Sequoyah saw a lone man making strange lines on a page. The lines made words. He wanted to make his own strange lines.

At last, he gave his people a bunch of letters on a page. They had a way to read and write! Sequoyah had helped his clan.

a as a in father or short as o in rival
e as a in hate or short as e in met
i as i in pique or short as i in pit

u as oo in fool or short as u in pull
v as u in but, nasalized.

Consonant Sounds.

in English, but approaching to k.—d nearly as in English, but approaching to t.

Word Works

Word Reading

A

fur	whir	term	spur	shirt
blur	third	fern	skirt	burn

Word Building

B

hatband   pancake   sunset

runway   moonbeam

Sight Words

C

more   these   years

all   from   write   number   who   now

A Look at Writing

Written by Eddie Lee

In the past, people did not write words. At first, they made big paintings on cave walls.

Later, in places like Egypt and China, people held tools with paint and made pictures. Each picture stood for something, like a sunset, a cat, or a hilltop.

A long time passed and people turned pictures into small lines. The lines stood for sounds. These lines made an alphabet!

Word Works

Word Reading

A

burn   wage   itch   sheep

quick   turn   stir   ace

Sight Words

B

great   does   also

there   use   other   about   want   only

Sentence Reading

C I will <u>use</u> this pen and you can <u>use</u> the <u>other</u> pen.

Is she <u>also</u> an <u>only</u> child?

It is <u>great</u> that you can ride a bike.

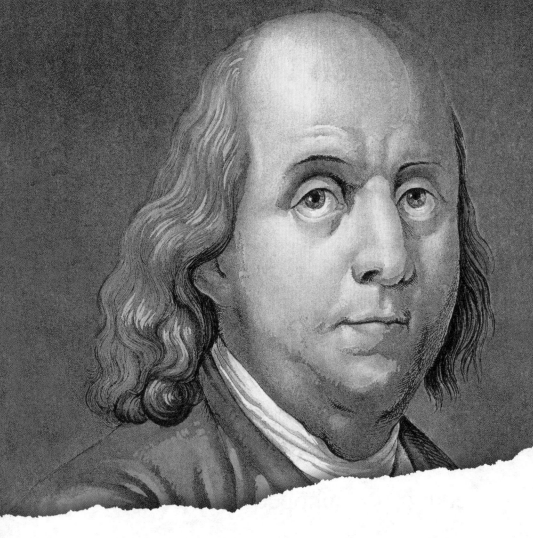

Ben Franklin's Great Ideas

When Ben was a child, he had good ideas. Ben liked swimming fast in the water. So Ben got wood and made paddles for his hands and feet.

Ben liked to write. He wanted to put his stories in the paper. Ben used a fake name so no one would think that a child wrote them. People liked them so the paper printed more.

Word Works

Letter and Sound Identification

A

ee   ea   oo   ch

st   cl   gr   sn

Word Reading

B

team	seed	hoot	stack
clap	crack	grip	snoop
running	seeing	clipped	buzzed

Sight Words

C

very   sentence   large

like   we   how   their

some   her   first   more

Ben Plans a Town

Towns were not like they are now.
If people needed a book, it was shipped
from England. Ben set up the first library.
Its job was to lend books.

Ben planned a way to stop fires, too. He got teams of men to go and help put them out. This was the first fire department.

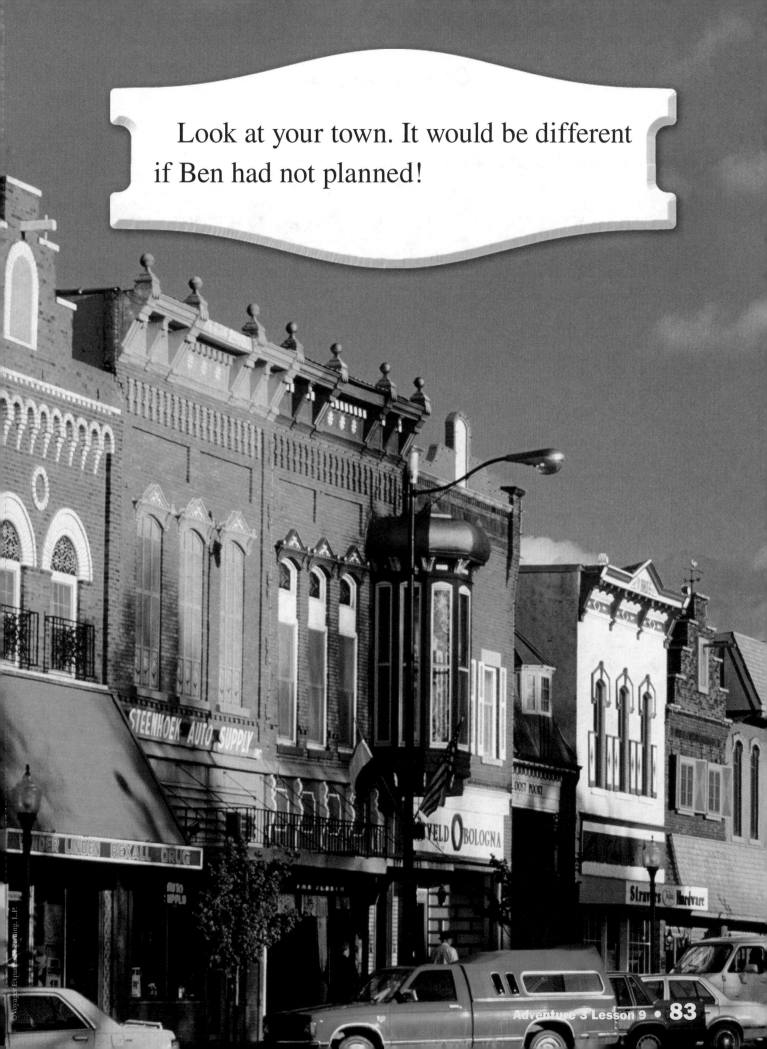

Look at your town. It would be different if Ben had not planned!

Quick Check

Letter and Sound Identification

A

1. cr w wr	2. ch ck cl	3. gr dge dr
4. ir dr tr	5. sl cr ck	6. oo ea mp
7. ea oo ay	8. wh ea wr	9. c sh g

Word Reading

B

1. pen pine pain	2. drape dirt drum	3. sledding slide slipped
4. seating skated shopping	5. fish ice isn't	6. page pace price
7. hire heap hide	8. brick burn bran	9. make mock meek

Sight Words

C

___ by	___ more	___ could	___ does
___ words	___ write	___ than	___ large
___ all	___ number	___ who	___ come
___ want	___ years	___ sentence	___ only
___ other	___ very	___ great	___ little
___ these	___ children	___ also	___ know

What can we learn from animals in the wild?

Word Works

Word Reading

A

small   halt   stall   fall   squall   wall

eat   food   soon   reach   gray   back

Sight Words

B

give   sound   work

many   come   little   very   sentence

Sentence Reading

C This small shop in the mall has <u>many</u> <u>little</u> tools.

<u>Many</u> people see ice on fall days.

The bell will <u>sound</u> for you to <u>come</u> to <u>work</u>.

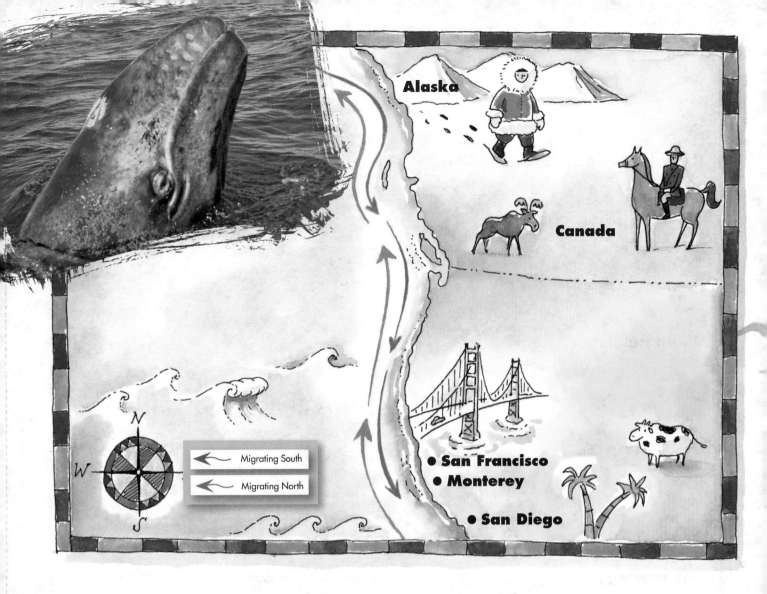

Gray Whales in the Sea

Written by Heera Kang • Illustrated by Steven Mach

Gray whales do not stay in one spot all year. When it gets very cold, whales swim to warm places. The whales eat as much food as they can to get ready. Then, they swim. Look at the way they go on the map.

When they reach their final stop, whales will have babies. Soon, big whales and small whales all swim back.

Word Works

Letter and Sound Identification

A

al   oa   ea   sh   ay

Word Reading

B

goat	toad	real	stall
roam	toast	day	foal

Sight Words

C

our   where   even

people   work   into   give   sound   water

My Ocean Journal

March 3

On this day, I worked with Dad on the boat. We floated on the water. The day was gray.

March 4

I put on my coat as little dolphins swam by us. In winter, gray whales swim to warm water. They swim home in the spring. This trip is called migration.

March 5

Our boat rocked. I groaned and slid. Then I fell into the ropes!

March 6

The sun popped out. The heat felt very nice.

March 7

A gray whale floated up. I gasped. It was huge!

Then it jumped and splashed me.

What a treat! I will call the whale Wally.

Word Works

Word Reading

A

trudge   lodge   bridge   budge   ledge

pool   eat   stand   stir   wall

Sight Words

B

new   any   right

then   our   where   even   does   know

Sentence Reading

C

I think my book is on the <u>right</u> side of the ledge.

Do you have <u>any</u> fudge for us to eat?

<u>Where</u> <u>does</u> your <u>new</u> coat go?

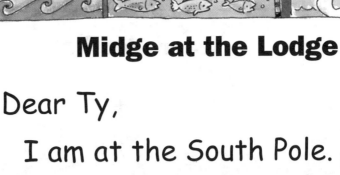

Midge at the Lodge

Dear Ty,

 I am at the South Pole. I am on migration. This new lodge is grand. The lodge has pools. One pool is filled with krill and fish. I sit under the bridge and eat. The pool is just like the sea! Will you come to this lodge with me on my next trip? Say yes!

 Midge

Word Works

Word Reading

A

bridge   fur   jerk   dredge   shirt

padded   swimming   running   slipped

Rule-Based Words

B

why   cry   we   no   shy   sky   pro

Sight Words

C

follow   form   around

their   make   number   could   know   years

Arctic Animals

Look at the Arctic on this map.
Do you know this cold place?

This big white bear has lots of fat.
It needs thick fur to help heat stay in.

This small fox has padded feet so it will
not make much sound on the ice.

The fat walrus stays in water and on the edge of the land. As it is swimming, it eats clams and fish.

The next sentence will tell you the big idea. The Arctic is a good home for animals that like the cold.

Quick Check

Letter and Sound Identification

A

1. st	gr	ck	2. ea	oo	oa	3. c	g	sh
4. oa	il	al	5. dge	ir	ing	6. ee	oa	er
7. er	i	ea	8. oa	ch	or	9. ea	al	oa

Word Reading

B

1. beat	boat	boot	2. hall	heal	hole	3. hedge	hitch	hat
4. floated	floating	falling	5. brick	bridge	bed	6. pry	pride	pine
7. stall	mall	malt	8. soap	snoop	sop	9. nick	nest	nice

Sight Words

C

___ new	___ our	___ around
___ sound	___ where	___ form
___ work	___ any	___ even
___ give	___ follow	___ right

Comprehension Check

Draw lines to match the sentences to the pictures.

My Ocean Journal

March 4

I put on my coat as little dolphins swam by us. In winter, gray whales swim to warm water. They swim home in the spring. This trip is migration.

March 5

Our boat rocked. I groaned and slid. Then I fell into the ropes!

March 7

A gray whale floated up. I gasped. It was huge! Then it jumped and splashed me. What a treat! I will call the whale Wally.

Write another journal entry. Draw a picture to go with your journal entry.

_____

_____

Word Works

Word Reading

A

boy read toy shoot clay

first ploy snack soy

Sight Words

B

move through another

each about some water around form

Sentence Reading

C

The boy needed to <u>move</u> <u>some</u> books.

Roy will shoot <u>another</u> ball <u>through</u> the hoop.

We <u>each</u> jumped for joy <u>around</u> the pole.

The Big Move

Think about moving each year to a new place. In fall, monarch butterflies flock to Mexico, where boys and girls rush to see them. The butterflies sleep through the winter in big fir trees.

In spring, their black and orange wings flap with joy as they follow the same path right back home. Next fall, the butterflies will go back to Mexico.

Word Works

Letter and Sound Identification

A

ea   oa   oo   ar   ee

sl   br   st   sw

Word Reading

B

start   cart   march   yard   barn   farm   part

sweets   food   toast   eating   bring   sleep

Sight Words

C

before   here   again

words   were   said   use   how   before

Butterflies and the Day of the Dead

The Day of the Dead is not a sad day.
In Mexico, it is a time to think of people
we loved.

First, we sing songs and eat great food.
I help push large carts with sweets.

After we eat, we start the march!
People wear costumes and men beat
drums.

Before it ends, the monarch butterflies flock in. Each year they dart around then sleep all winter. When they fly, we jump and clap. It is the best part!

Word Works

Word Reading

A

train   steam   pail   grand

plain   aim   brain   small

Sight Words

B

change   away   house

more   there   these   would   through   form

Sentence Reading

C

The grand plan will <u>change</u>.

I will ride the train to the end of <u>these</u> tracks.

Aim the ball, then toss it <u>away</u> from the <u>house</u>.

You must do <u>more</u> to train your dog.

African Animals on the Move

In winter, wildebeests migrate far to look for tall grass. If you want to see them, take a trip to the African plains.

Wildebeests form herds. Strong males keep the herd safe. There is a place for the small, weak ones in the herd too. Each day wildebeests move to look for grass. Herds end up in dark woods to rest. On the next day, herds move even farther to eat good grass.

Word Works

Letter and Sound Identification

A   ee   oo   ar   ai   or   er

Word Reading

B   short   born   torch   store   tore   chore

feel   wood   plains   far   herd

Sight Words

C   because   mother   air

from   what   your   who   does   large

Will Zain Stay?

Written by Dan Davis • Illustrated by Damian Ward

"I want to stay, too!" Zain tells Dad.
Zain does not want to move this winter. He
thinks he can stay in the plains with
a herd of wild horses. His pal, Koy, will
stay also.

"Help!" wails Pudge. Zain spots his little brother. A hyena is running for his tail! Is there any chance to catch up? Zain and Dad race to save Pudge. They force the hyena to flee.

"I will stay with our herd," Zain tells
Dad. "Pudge does need a big brother."

Quick Check

Letter and Sound Identification

A

1. oa	oy	ea	2. ar	ai	er	3. e	al	cl
4. dge	dr	sh	5. sl	ch	c	6. wh	er	ay
7. j	ee	y	8. oa	ai	ea	9. oa	oy	ol

Word Reading

B

1. felt	feed	fed	2. real	rail	rule	3. short	soar	share
4. green	grain	gray	5. fame	frame	farm	6. joy	join	jolt
7. why	we	wheel	8. smell	small	shell	9. got	good	goat

Sight Words

C

___ new	___ any	___ form	___ away
___ sound	___ before	___ even	___ house
___ work	___ another	___ change	___ move
___ give	___ because	___ again	___ mother
___ our	___ follow	___ through	___ here
___ where	___ around	___ air	___ right

How are families different?

Word Works

Word Reading

A

whip	smiles	coat	tail	check
stir	asked	best	smelled	time

Multisyllabic Words

B picnic   insect   skillet   napkin   insist

Sight Words

C

picture   different   animal   laugh

great   from   about   people   come   before

Sentence Reading

D

It's <u>about</u> time to take a <u>picture</u>!

Insects can't <u>come</u> to my picnic.

Isn't there food for the <u>animal</u>?

<u>People</u> look <u>different</u> when they smile and <u>laugh</u>.

Family Dinner

My name is Ben. My cousin Tom and I help Grandma make dinner. Tom gets the napkins. I stir the meat in the skillet.

Dad was away at work, but now he's home, too. "I like it when we're all here," Dad says.

Grandma smiles and agrees.

"Where is Jan?" Tom asks.

Jan comes in.

"Jan came because she smelled dinner!" says Dad.

We laugh. Dinner is the best time in our house.

Word Works

Letter and Sound Identification

A

ou	ea	ai	er	ar
ch	cl	kn	gr	wr

Word Reading

B

round   stark   beach   cloud   knead

rainstorm   backyard   antics

Multisyllabic Words

C

sister   perfect   batter   better

Sight Words

D

learn   study   watch

more   later   there   these

because   he's   we're   I'll

My Cousin and Me

Grandma munched a carrot. She said,
"When you were small, you all played. Jan,
Tom, and Ben, you were funny!"

"Tom and I enjoyed playing ball," I said.

The next day, Tom and I played ball in the backyard with my dad. The ground was wet from a rainstorm, but the clouds had passed.

Tom was the batter. He tripped and fell. Then I slipped and fell, too.

Dad laughed at our antics. "You still are funny! Tom, why not try again? Take a turn," Dad said.

Then Tom hit the ball and I cheered.

I am glad that Tom lives here. It is so
much better with him here. We are cousins,
but it is different. He seems like my brother.

Word Works

Word Reading

A

letter   found   wring   float

loud   until   visit

Multisyllabic Words

B

solo   skater   clover   spider   crater

Sight Words

C

between   school   country

write   here   know   watch   again   I'm

Sentence Reading

D

I'll <u>watch</u> until you go into the <u>school</u>.

She must wring out her wet napkin <u>again</u>.

My mother plans to visit that <u>country</u> and send

me a letter.

<u>I'm</u> standing <u>between</u> Mark and Gail.

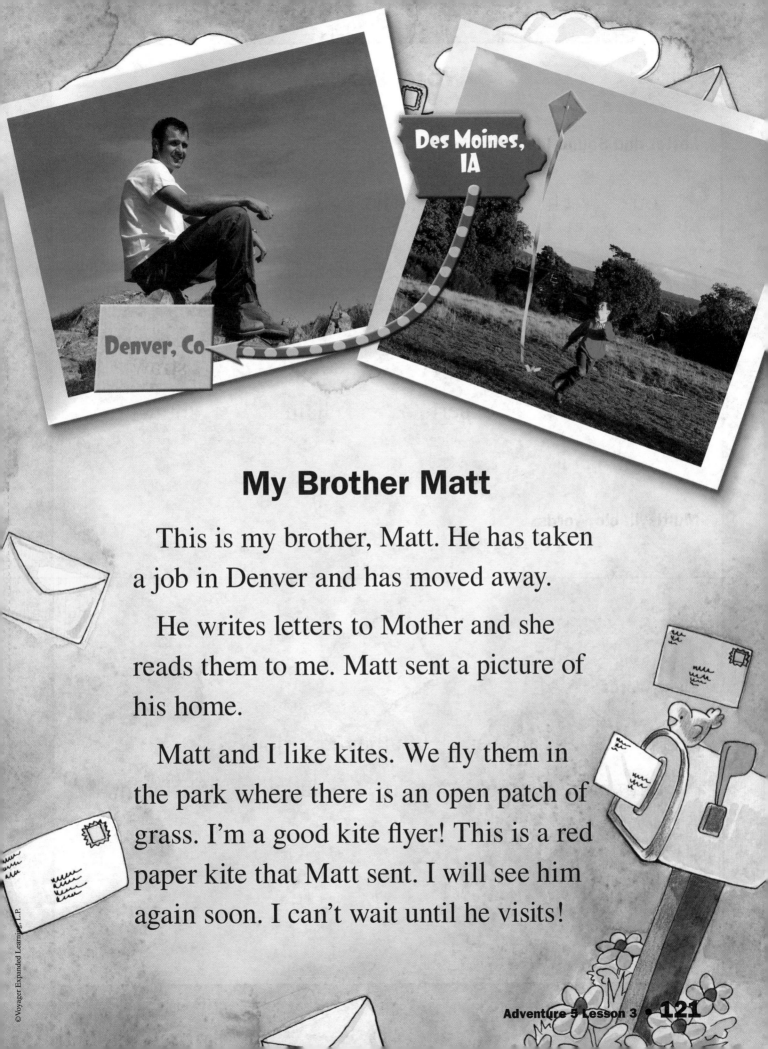

Des Moines, IA

Denver, Co

My Brother Matt

This is my brother, Matt. He has taken a job in Denver and has moved away.

He writes letters to Mother and she reads them to me. Matt sent a picture of his home.

Matt and I like kites. We fly them in the park where there is an open patch of grass. I'm a good kite flyer! This is a red paper kite that Matt sent. I will see him again soon. I can't wait until he visits!

© Voyager Expanded Learning L.P.

Word Works

Letter and Sound Identification

A ou   ch   ai   sh   aw   th   oi

Word Reading

B
claw   lawn   sound   straw

stout   expert   chain   brawl

Multisyllabic Words

C navy   deny   lady   shaken   reply

Sight Words

D   answer   father   don't

animal   isn't   we're   laugh   different

Matt and His Fun Trips

Written by Theresa Volpe • Illustrated by Veronica Rooney

Matt has a job flying airplanes. He's an expert. When my red kite floats way up near the clouds, I think about him. This morning I got a letter and a book Matt mailed.

Mother opened the letter:

Mother, don't worry. My plane takes many people to fun places. I can take trips too. Study the book, little brother! Love, Matt

On one trip Matt went to a ranch with large animals. He fed them bunches of straw and clover. He rode a stout pony down a dirt trail. Then he had to fly to a country far away.

The book was packed with neat maps
from all over the world. I can look up the
places where Matt went on his plane.

Quick Check

Letter and Sound Identification

1. ou	oo	oy	2. ar	ea	ai	3. oo	oy	or
4. oo	or	oa	5. ai	ee	er	6. igh	ar	ai
7. aw	ar	ai	8. br	sl	bl	9. th	sh	st

Word Reading

1. got	good	goat	2. mouth	moth	most	3. cram	crawl	crate
4. sped	speeder	spider	5. wing	wring	wrong	6. insect	insist	inside
7. shouted	showed	shouter	8. rely	reply	real	9. shawl	shell	saw

Sight Words

___ picture   ___ different   ___ animal

___ laugh   ___ learn   ___ study

___ watch   ___ between   ___ school

___ country   ___ answer   ___ father

___ don't

Comprehension Check

Read the passage "Matt and His Fun Trips" and answer the questions.

1. Who are the characters in this story?

_____

_____

2. When Matt went on his trip to the ranch, what animal did he ride?

_____

_____

3. What did Matt do after visiting the ranch?

_____

_____

4. What does the narrator do with the book of maps Matt sent him?

_____

_____

Word Works

Word Reading

A

cold   spine   bolt   scold

smug   same   told   baseball   twins

Multisyllabic Words

B

program   tiny   began   concert   object

Sight Words

C

eye   world   together

follow   another   very   it's   he's

Sentence Reading

D

Where in the <u>world</u> is the land <u>very</u> cold?

We are told <u>another</u> new word each day.

I felt a tiny object in my <u>eye</u>.

This bolt will hold the toy car <u>together</u>.

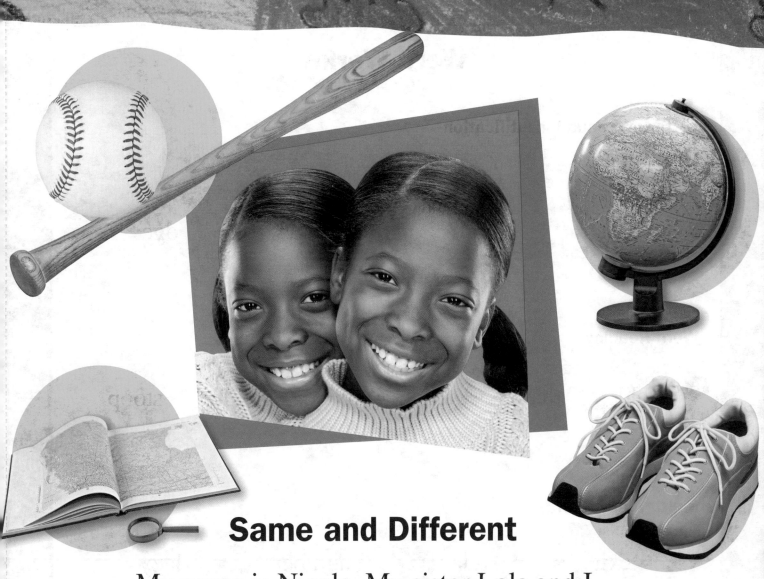

Same and Different

My name is Nicole. My sister Lola and I are twins, which means we look the same. We are just as old. We both have dark hair. We even have the same brown eyes!

But we do not like the same things. I like to play baseball and go running. My sister likes to watch programs and hear concerts from around the world. She reads books about the world, and I like to run on it!

Word Works

Letter and Sound Identification

A

ol	ai	aw	oo
sh	th	wh	dge

Word Reading

B

fold   thaw   smolder   wedge   plain   stoop

Multisyllabic Words

C

exit	relax	number	lazy
contrast	subject	extra	funny

Sight Words

D

every	friends	story	always
through	who	world	together

©Voyager Expanded Learning, L.P.

Nicole and Lola

Written by Tony Garcia • Illustrated by Carol Koeller

Nicole and Lola look like each other.
Friends often get them mixed up. It's
funny when people think Nicole is Lola
or Lola is Nicole!

Both girls go to the same school.
But they don't like the same subjects.

Lola likes to study history, but Nicole
likes to play ball in gym class.

Dad helps Lola read about the world.

Mom runs with Nicole.

Lola likes to tell Nicole about history subjects. Nicole asks Lola to run and play ball with her.

But at the end of the day, Nicole and Lola like to relax together!

Word Works

Word Reading

A

slight   cheek   night   fight   spout   sigh

home   sling   names   hope   start

Multisyllabic Words

B

invite   twenty   prepare   member   summer   beside

Sight Words

C

thought   both   group

study   change   house   between   country   school

Sentence Reading

D

At night there is no light in the <u>house</u>.

In high <u>school</u>, you may <u>study</u> in a <u>group</u>.

We <u>thought</u> the <u>country</u> was too cold.

There is a slight <u>change</u> to <u>both</u> classes.

Reunion: June 22
Prepare for a big dinner and party!

Summer Reunion

Our family lives all over the country. So every summer, we meet in our hometown.

This year Mom is planning the reunion. We might prepare a big dinner one night.

Mom says we should start by making a list of names of our family members. Soon we will send letters to invite them. I will make a welcome banner. I hope they all can come!

Word Works

Letter and Sound Identification

A

ow   ee   oo   oa   ou

Word Reading

B

glow   beach   sow   frown   speed   grown

near   throw   chatting   bow   catch   growl

Multisyllabic Words

C

decide   yummy   happens   begin

Sight Words

D

example   something   live

eye   learn   father   story   every   world

Getting Together

Is all of your family near you? It is hard to see family when they live far away. Some may live near the beach. Others may live in towns where it snows. Reunions bring everyone together.

What happens at reunions? There is playing, eating, and chatting!

Some people begin games. They throw balls, toss balloons, or play cards.

There is always something yummy to eat between games! For example, there might be burgers or cupcakes.

©Voyager Expanded Learning, L.P.

Some people just like to sit and chat. It's a time to catch up with a sister or cousin. You can see how much a new baby has grown.

Many people stay late into the night. No one wants to go home! They may leave with a frown. But they will all show up with a smile to repeat the fun next year.

©Voyager Expanded Learning, L.P.

Quick Check

Letter and Sound Identification

A

1. oo	ol	oy	2. igh	ee	ir	3. ow	oa	ol
4. ay	oa	oo	5. o	er	ea	6. aw	er	or
7. ur	ou	ar	8. igh	oy	aw	9. ar	ow	ai

Word Reading

B

1. even	exit	I've	2. good	gold	got	3. rapid	rubbed	rip
4. humming	hunt	human	5. seat	sight	sit	6. lasting	lost	lazy
7. grow	grab	green	8. seller	smelled	smolder	9. invest	invite	inside

Sight Words

C

___ eye	___ world	___ together
___ every	___ friends	___ story
___ always	___ thought	___ both
___ group	___ example	___ something
___ live	___ picture	___ different
___ animal	___ laugh	___ learn
___ study	___ watch	___ between
___ school	___ country	___ answer
___ father	___ don't	

How do plants and animals survive everywhere?

Word Works

Word Reading

A

tie packed die sunshine rich

branches flight place lie warm

Multisyllabic Words

B detail fifteen target layer forest shower

Sight Words

C

color important enough surface

picture something example always group close

Sentence Reading

D It's <u>important</u> to keep the <u>surface</u> clean.

After the hot shower, her skin was a bright red <u>color</u>.

Do you have <u>enough</u> string to tie the <u>group</u> of fifteen

branches?

Mold <u>always</u> grows on the layer of leaves in the forest.

top layer

middle layer

bottom layer

Sunny and Wet Today

Written by Danielle Hammelef

A tropical rain forest is packed with plants in bright colors. It is a warm, wet place. There are birds in flight, insects crawling, and animals hiding.

High at the forest top, the branches of tall trees grow together like a thick, green roof.

Small trees and plants grow under that roof. They don't get as much sunshine or rain.

Leaves die and fall on the ground. They make a rich surface. New plants always come up again.

Word Works

Letter and Sound Identification

A

ph	th	ch	sh	wh
or	ai	oo	ou	ea

Word Reading

B

phone   graph   screech   phase   swoop

phrase   howl   snatch   beak   trunk

Multisyllabic Words

C

table   yellow   stable   purple   monkey

rattle   amaze   devour   jungle

Sight Words

D

heard   listen   special

change   thought   both   together   enough   color

What Lives in a Rain Forest?

The plants, birds, and insects living in the rain forest will amaze you! What photos will you take?

The pitcher plant attracts insects with a special smell. When something falls in the flower, it can't get out. Then the plant devours it!

Howler monkeys live in the top branches of trees. They are the loudest land animals in the world. Listen! Their loud screech can be heard 3 miles away.

Look at the colorful macaw as it swoops down to snatch a snack! These birds can be many bright colors like red, blue, yellow, and purple. They have strong beaks that can crack open nuts, seeds, and even coconuts! Macaws make their nests in holes of jungle trees. These birds can live to be 80 years old.

Word Works

Letter and Sound Identification

A
oa   ee   au   ol   al   ar

Word Reading

B
haul   fault   target   pause   salt   cause

giant   coral   bottom   harbor   until

Sight Words

C
question   notice   ocean

answer   important   friends   heard   listen

Sentence Reading

D
I will pause before I <u>answer</u> your <u>question</u>.

I didn't <u>notice</u> until we hit the bottom.

Haul the giant fish back to the <u>ocean</u>.

It is <u>important</u> that we find the cause of the problem.

Life in the Salty Sea

Have you ever paused and thought about what lives deep under the ocean? Think about the questions you could ask a starfish or coral. Have you ever noticed the giant kelp?

The ocean has layers. Some ocean life stays on the bottom. Other kinds float close to the surface. Kelp gets energy from the sun. Starfish and coral get energy from small plants and animals in the water.

Word Works

Letter and Sound Identification

A au   ie   aw   ow   ea   oo

Word Reading

B phone   lie   photo   tie   snow   draw

fish   green   pause   look   back   down

Multisyllabic Words

C sharpen   table   nibble   forget

rattle   eager   middle   captain

Sight Words

D   early   island   minute

questions   ocean   special   thought

live   answer   watch

Water Surprise

I showed up early for the boat tour. I was eager to see what lives under the ocean. The bottom of the boat was glass and showed clear blue water.

"There are fish below," said Gerard, our captain, "but there are plants and insects, too."

I saw a sea anemone on a rock with green kelp. The kelp looked like thin paper. A purple fish nibbled on it.

The boat paused near a small island. "Look over the side and watch for an insect," said Gerard.

I looked down in the water for a minute. Then I jumped!

An insect that looked like a spider startled me. "Water striders use their middle and back legs to run on water," said Gerard.

That was a surprise!

Quick Check

Letter and Sound Identification

A

1. ou ie igh	2. ai ea ar	3. au oy ea
4. ol oo oa	5. ir ie ee	6. ou ol el
7. aw ar wh	8. oo ou aw	9. sh pl ph

Word Reading

B

1. try the tie	2. follow phone photo	3. fresh forest forget
4. fog fault flat	5. write wren wrote	6. tapped tray table
7. below blow bully	8. think thank trunk	9. sight slide slight

Sight Words

C

___ heard	___ question	___ early	___ color
___ listen	___ notice	___ island	___ important
___ special	___ ocean	___ minute	___ enough
___ surface			

©Voyager Expanded Learning, L.P.

Comprehension Check

Read the passage "Water Surprise" and answer the questions.

1. Why did the boy show up early for the boat tour?

_____

_____

2. What did the kelp look like?

_____

3. Where did the boat pause?

_____

4. What did the boy see in the water that made him jump?

_____

5. What did the water strider look like?

_____

Word Works

Word Reading

A
join   soil   quest   flew   choice

moist   swoop   curved   blooming

Multisyllabic Words

B
refuse   center   cactus   flower   woodpecker

Sight Words

C
travel   hours   toward   desert

minutes   island   air   away   both   almost   surface

Sentence Reading

D
The moist <u>surface</u> helped the flowers grow.

It took <u>almost</u> two <u>hours</u> to sort the coins.

We <u>both</u> refuse to join this quest.

Zoila will <u>travel</u> <u>toward</u> the <u>desert</u>.

Going Home

The woodpecker was glad. He was almost there. He had traveled for hours in the hot desert.

He swooped down toward the tall cactus. Its four curved branches pointed to the sky. Its white flowers had bloomed in the cool, night air.

The woodpecker flew inside the hole in the center of the cactus. Home at last!

Word Works

Letter and Sound Identification

A

ie   oo   ai   ay   ow   ee

Word Reading

B

field   chief   brief   yield

below   serve   shapes   pieces

Word Building

C

dry   lady   rely   try   baby

dries   ladies   relied   tried   babies

Sight Words

D

once   area   usually

every   something   always

watch   color   important

Which Plants Live in Hot Deserts?

A tumbleweed grows in desert soil until strong winds blow. Once the leaves and branches pull away from the roots, these plants roll around in dry fields. They have seeds that make new plants.

The cactus plant has white flowers and usually yields fruit that is green and red. Some people may even serve pieces of cactus fruit on their dinner table!

Other plants grow flowers that are red, yellow, gold, and pink. They may wait for rain and then bloom for a brief time.

A desert is not just an area of sand and sun. It yields many living things. You can see it and believe it. Plants bloom in all shapes and colors!

Word Works

Letter and Sound Identification

A

ea	oa	al	ow	oi
ck	ch	ph	kn	igh

Word Reading

B

eagle   fly   soar   place   mountain

rocky   reach   falcon   smaller

Sight Words

C

walk   above   several

once   area   usually   eye

follow   does   there   their

Sentence Reading

D

I will <u>walk</u> to a rocky <u>area</u> by the brook.

<u>Their</u> map of the world is torn.

I <u>usually</u> take my phone with me when I <u>follow</u> a trail.

The bird soared <u>above</u> <u>several</u> clouds.

Rocky Mountain Birds

Walk into the Rocky Mountains and look up. Tall forest trees reach to the sky. Eagles nest in treetops. Falcons soar in the cliffs above. Swans swim along rivers below. In each tree, smaller birds sing cheerful songs.

The high, open places are important. The trees are important too. Thousands of birds call them their home.

Word Works

Letter and Sound Identification

A

ai   ee   oa   oo   ea   oi

Word Reading

B

head   stain   sweep   dread   health   noise

berry   berries   shrubs   wings   rare   might

Multisyllabic Words

C

major   human   nectar   falcon

gobbles   ahead   sudden

Sight Words

D

though   suddenly   guide

work   very   children   picture

another   thought   listen   group

A Rare Sight

Written by Sunny Dedich • Illustrated by Vicki Learner

"Listen," says Ingrid, our guide. We are
bird-watching. We listen as a hummingbird
flaps its wings really fast. It makes a
humming noise. We see it drink nectar
from a flower with red petals. Suddenly it
dashes away. I almost got a picture!

"Stay together, children," says Ingrid. "We might see a falcon. They are rare, though."

Next we see a mountain bluebird. It gobbles berries in the shrubs.

The last bird we see sits high up on a tree branch. It turns its head slowly. Then it spots something ahead and zooms away in a flash.

It was a young falcon!

Quick Check

Letter and Sound Identification

A

1. ou	ie	ea	2. ph	pr	pl	3. ee	al	ir
4. oo	oa	ai	5. ir	ie	er	6. oi	er	ea
7. oi	ou	ai	8. igh	or	ir	9. ar	au	ow

Word Reading

B

1. head	heat	hit	2. piece	place	press	3. launch	lunch	lots
4. set	swat	sweat	5. nose	noise	knots	6. setting	sadden	sudden
7. farther	father	fatter	8. barking	braking	baking	9. sung	swung	sang

Sight Words

C

___ important	___ area	___ several
___ travel	___ question	___ though
___ hours	___ notice	___ color
___ toward	___ ocean	___ island
___ heard	___ early	___ surface
___ listen	___ usually	___ minute
___ special	___ walk	___ suddenly
___ desert	___ above	___ guide
___ once	___ enough	

Timed Reading Log

	Passage Title	Words Per Minute
1		
2		
3		
4		
5		
6		
7		
8		
9		
10		
11		
12		
13		
14		
15		
16		
17		
18		
19		
20		

Fluency Chart

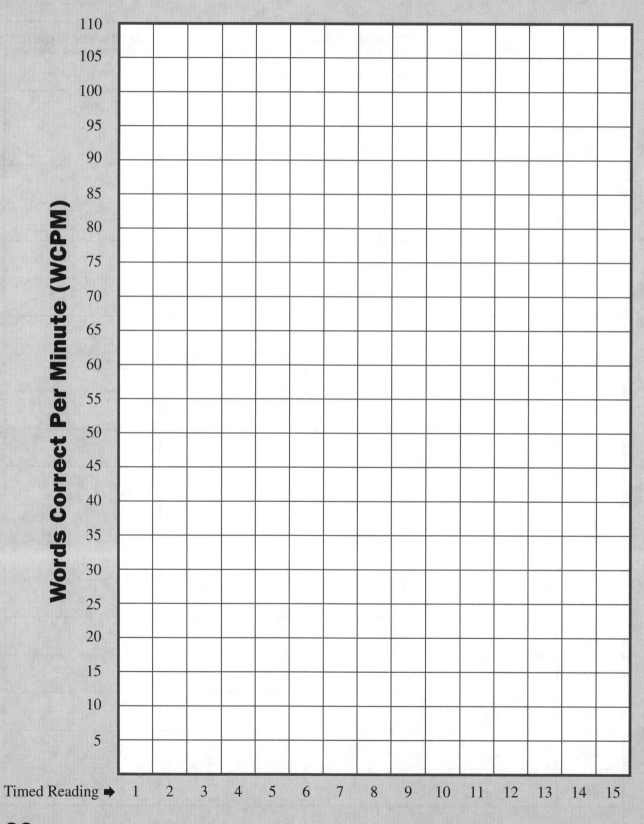

Words Correct Per Minute (WCPM)

110
105
100
95
90
85
80
75
70
65
60
55
50
45
40
35
30
25
20
15
10
5

Timed Reading ➡ 1 2 3 4 5 6 7 8 9 10 11 12 13 14 15

Vocabulary Log

V ► **Adventure 1**

V ► **Adventure 2**

Vocabulary Log

V ► Adventure 3

V ► Adventure 4

C4

Vocabulary Log

V ► Adventure 5

V ► Adventure 6

Word Families

-at	-an	-op	-ip	-ap
bat	man	cop	dip	cap
hat	tan	hop	lip	gap
pat	ran	pop	sip	map
rat	fan	top	clip	nap
that	plan	flop	flip	clap
flat	pan	plop	slip	flap
mat	can	stop	trip	snap
fat				trap

-ug	-ill	-ell	-ick	-ack
dug	will	well	sick	tack
rug	till	tell	tick	sack
hug	mill	fell	nick	rack
tug	fill	sell	pick	lack
lug	drill	bell	click	stack
slug	grill	shell	slick	crack
bug				

-ock	-ing	-ash	-est	-in
clock	sing	mash	rest	pin
dock	ring	trash	best	fin
sock	king	cash	nest	spin
rock	wing	gash	test	thin
lock	bring	sash	pest	chin
stock	cling	flash	crest	grin
block	sting	smash	vest	skin
	thing	dash		twin

Word Families

-ink
sink
link
pink
wink
think
blink
drink

-unk
sunk
dunk
junk
chunk
stunk
trunk

-ake
bake
cake
fake
shake
lake
quake
wake

-ate
rate
fate
mate
date
state
crate
late

-ide
side
tide
ride
hide
slide
glide
bride

-ine
mine
fine
pine
vine
shine
whine
line

-ice
rice
price
dice
slice
nice
mice

-eat
neat
heat
treat
seat
beat

-ir
sir
stir
fir

-ail
rail
pail
nail
tail
wail

-ain
rain
pain
plain
drain
stain

-ank
thank
plank
bank
crank
sank
drank
blank

-id
kid
did
bid
lid
hid

-ad
bad
sad
pad
mad
dad

-ed
red
led
bed
sped
shed

Sight Words

► **Adventure 1**

to	_____	his	_____	from	_____
the	_____	was	_____	have	_____
on	_____	as	_____	your	_____
you	_____	he	_____	or	_____
it	_____	that	_____	one	_____
for	_____	with	_____	this	_____
they	_____	we	_____	of	_____
are	_____	be	_____	what	_____
said	_____	put	_____	were	_____

► **Adventure 2**

make	_____	into	_____	would	_____
out	_____	there	_____	way	_____
use	_____	each	_____	people	_____
she	_____	many	_____	water	_____
her	_____	like	_____	first	_____
their	_____	how	_____	do	_____
some	_____	so	_____	about	_____
call	_____	may	_____	now	_____

Sight Words

► Adventure 3

who	____	know	____	also	____
could	____	all	____	does	____
words	____	only	____	very	____
by	____	children	____	sentence	____
than	____	other	____	large	____
come	____	number	____	these	____
want	____	write	____	more	____
little	____	great	____	years	____

► Adventure 4

give	____	right	____	here	____
sound	____	follow	____	again	____
work	____	form	____	change	____
our	____	around	____	away	____
where	____	move	____	house	____
even	____	before	____	because	____
new	____	another	____	mother	____
any	____	through	____	air	____

Sight Words

 ► **Adventure 5**

picture	_____	country	_____	story	_____
different	_____	answer	_____	thought	_____
animal	_____	father	_____	both	_____
laugh	_____	don't	_____	group	_____
learn	_____	eye	_____	example	_____
study	_____	world	_____	something	_____
watch	_____	together	_____	live	_____
between	_____	every	_____	never	_____
school	_____	always	_____		

 ► **Adventure 6**

color	_____	ocean	_____	area	_____
important	_____	early	_____	usually	_____
enough	_____	island	_____	above	_____
surface	_____	minute	_____	several	_____
heard	_____	travel	_____	though	_____
listen	_____	hours	_____	suddenly	_____
special	_____	toward	_____	guide	_____
question	_____	desert	_____	walk	_____
notice	_____	once	_____	different	_____